TEESSIDE STEEL

The Final Years

Mike Guess

AMBERLEY

The author.

First published 2019

Amberley Publishing
The Hill, Stroud
Gloucestershire, GL5 4EP

www.amberleybooks.com

British Library Cataloguing in Publication Data.
A catalogue record for this book is available from the British Library.

ISBN 978 1 4456 8523 6 (print)
ISBN 978 1 4456 8524 3 (ebook)

Origination by Amberley Publishing.
Printed in Great Britain.

Introduction

At 07.30 on 13 August 1979, an old hand-operated clocking machine straight out of the Arc announced the start of my apprenticeship and the first day of my life at the steelworks at Teesside.

In 1979, just the electrical apprentice intake was forty; split into four groups of ten, we each had our own instructor. Mechanical and structural apprentices of about the same number made for quite a large intake, but it was the last year to see such an amount of new apprentices.

My first introduction to work was on a 'works special', a green bus with an open back door and a very noisy diesel engine that delivered me to the gates of Clay Lane Furnaces and the training centre. This was a journey I repeated several times until I bought a bike in my first year out of the training centre, when I needed to get to Redcar Works.

I was an apprentice with a few months' training when we went on a plant visit. As I remember, we walked through the older Cleveland Works, past what was pointed out as the Arc Plant and on to the BOS Plant. We never got to see the old mills, although I did see them in later years. At the time they were just something on the way to somewhere, and back then I wasn't really interested in that.

The image portrayed on the news when reporting on the numerous cutbacks and closures was the blast furnace at the steelworks. The steelworks down the road at Lackenby, although huge, was not often noticed by reporters. The blast furnace produced the liquid iron that was poured (tapped) into torpedoes standing under the furnace. These were then pulled by a locomotive along the track the couple of miles to the steelmaking plant (BOS Plant) at the Lackenby Works at Grangetown.

During this time of closure, the mills had an advantage in that they didn't need Teesside steel in order to roll slabs or ingots, which they could source from anywhere, and consequently survived the end of the steelmaking side of the works.

It is with great regret that I did not have an interest in the history around me in those days; even though I always had a camera, I didn't record the disappearing world that I was living in.

With an increased interest in local and industrial history, however, the mothball, restart and eventual closing of iron and steelmaking on Teesside was something that I was not going to fail to record. It was almost an obligation to future generations of what happened to us.

These are some of my photographs from my time working at the steelworks on Teesside.

Just after midday on 18 April 2012, the new SSI workforce wait for the first slab cast of the new era to travel down Slab No. 2, Strand No. 2, roller table.

Redcar Power Station, as seen from halfway up the Redcar blast furnace.

One of the stacker machines in the stockyards of the Redcar Works.

The sinter plant at Redcar Works, looking towards the electrostatic precipitators. The purpose of these was to remove the dust from the gas before it went up the chimney.

A barrel reclaimer, again at the stockyards of Redcar Works. These were the machines that picked up the ingredients from the stockyards and either put them on to conveyors or placed them into piles (blending).

A barrel reclaimer and a stacker on the coal side after a downpour had filled up the conveyors.

A view of the Redcar blast furnace from the western side, showing the charge conveyor. On the restart with SSI I had the chance to look around. I never got to work on the Redcar furnace, only the Cleveland iron furnaces.

A view from the inside of the furnace from when it was having a partial reline during the SSI restart. The lower staves were replaced and this photograph shows where they have been removed.

Here we see a stave waiting to be fixed into position. Behind are the new ones that have already been completed. The platform that I am standing on was not the bottom of the furnace, but a good few metres higher. At this time, the hearth was getting blocked out.

A view of two of the tap hole positions when the furnace was not producing, a completely different scene from when it would have been producing iron continuously. The two machines at the front lift off the lids that covered the iron running from the furnace.

Some of the tuyeres that delivered the hot blast into the furnace. Not having worked at the Redcar blast furnace, to me it seemed it was all pipes for the water cooling.

Redcar blast furnace in the evening sun. The west casthouse can also be seen, as well as the tops of the stoves.

Some work
being carried
out on the iron
ponds next
to the blast
furnace. I am
not sure if they
are preparing
them or digging
out the iron.

The Redcar coke oven battery with the pusher cars parked up at the end. The coke ovens
was another place I never worked, and although offered a position there in 2010, this wasn't
somewhere I wanted to work.

Here we see the parked-up pusher cars. These were used to push the formed coke out of the battery into another car on the other side.

Torpedo ladle No. 43 discharges its molten iron into the ponds just along from the blast furnace. This was done if there was a problem at steelmaking, or perhaps a problem with the iron chemistry.

11

Another view of the same process of ponding iron into specially constructed berms. The tipping of the molten iron quite often gave off masses of orange fumes that didn't go down too well with everybody.

The blast furnace and coke ovens' gasholders, as seen from the South Gare Road. This went past the boundary fence, giving good views of the blast furnace and the tapping of iron into waiting torpedoes.

Two torpedoes being returned to the blast furnace are captured as they pass the back of Steel House over the 'Fleet', one of many becks that went through the site.

South Bank coke ovens and the Wilputte quencher producing lots of steam clouds after quenching a car of white-hot coke.

Newly formed coke being pushed from an oven into the coke car that will then travel down the track to the Wilputte quencher, where it is doused in water.

The South Bank coke ovens and a different view of the iconic bunker that everyone recognises at Teesside.

A photograph of the Simons quencher in front of where the original battery would have been. The photograph was taken from what was the Clay Lane furnaces.

Another view of the battery at South Bank coke ovens, and a little bit of smoke is being released from the process.

South Bank coke ovens, showing the blended stock bunkers. These were demolished sometime after this image was taken and were not there when I visited later. With nearly all my work life being based at the steelmaking at the Lackenby side of the works, most of the next photographs are from my time there.

The steelmaking plant at the Lackenby end of the Teesside site is known as the BOS (Basic Oxygen Steelmaking) plant.

The BOS plant, seen from the scrap bay. This area was usually full of scrap, but when we became SSI we had to source our scrap from far and wide and a lot of it wasn't very good. On one occasion prior to the SSI days we had a lot of bales made up from tin cans. This brought a plague of flies into the whole steelmaking plant.

Before the desulphurisation plant was built, the iron was desulphurised at the Polysius Plant. What was left of it is on the right of this photograph and I believe the silo was still used to store the powder and transfer it to the desulphurisation plant.

Torpedo No. 42, which has travelled from the iron plant blast furnace, arrives in position to pour its iron content into a waiting hot metal ladle in the pit below.

One of the new locos on its first visit to the BOS plant to test that it will fit into the pouring position. When SSI took over they decided to replace the older locomotives with this type. After our closure they went to Scunthorpe, I believe.

A well-lit view of the ladle bay showing the ladle preheaters and the feeder cranes to the Concast plant. It looks very congested with ladles in various conditions. Ladles could move into and out of the bay by transfer cars coming from the vessels to the right and secondary steelmaking to the left.

High up in the BOS building on the lance crane track, we look down at the lance carriages and water-cooled hoods that take away the hot gasses and dust to the gas cleaning systems. The gasses then pass through the chimneys, where the carbon monoxide was ignited and flared off. This could be seen for miles, especially at night, when they lit up the sky.

The charging side of the vessels, with what looks like one blowing.

This photograph shows the vessels as they were when production paused. The B vessel is seen undergoing repair.

The dart machine. The process of adding a refractory dart was to stop the flow of steel into the casting ladle that was in position below the vessel. When the vessel was tilted to allow the steel to pour through the tap hole, the dart would block the hole when the slag was about to go through and stop it from transferring into the ladle.

The dart machine inside A vessel.

The doors of A vessel, with the glow of the steel within. Aluminium bars on the pallet to the right would be thrown down a shute into the ladle below.

The full ladle in position on the flushing station after the steel in the vessel had been tapped into it. The flushing station was the first step in adjusting the make-up of the steel.

The ladle, waiting on the transfer car to accept the first tap of steel of the SSI era. The bottom of the vessel can be seen with a lot of sparks falling down from the effects of an over-enthusiastic blow.

Looking from the Concast plant into the BOS ladle bay, probably during a night shift. Compare this 2009 photograph with the view from 2015, on page 19, when it had much better lighting.

The same ladle bay but seen from the other end, in the ladle prep area. One of the feeder cranes is just placing a lid on a ladle. When the ladle came back from the Concast, this was where they would get new plates fitted to the gates.

A ladle sat on the pad having a gate prepared for some new plates before going back into the fleet.

A ladle undergoing repair. It looks pretty cold, so it might have a lot wrong with it. The bottom of the photograph shows a good view of the gate system swung open.

Three ladles under repair or being relined with refractory bricks by our brickies.

Ladle No. 37 in the teeming bay is seen being emptied into a hot metal ladle for the steel to be returned to the vessel. This might have been returned with some steel from the Concast.

Again in the teeming bay, this ladle was too full for safe casting so has had some steel tipped out onto the floor. This will be re-entered into the vessel as scrap later on.

A ladle having just finished casting in the Concast plant is then emptied into a slag pot. If calculations were correct, then the contents of the pot should be mainly slag.

Another photograph of the same process but at a different ladle. The chains were hooked onto the ladle by an operator on the ground floor.

Looking from the SL (Scandinavian Lance) station into the ladle bay the sun streams through the roof and is caught in all the smoke and dust that was a constant presence, although a lot better than previous years.

On the same day but looking back towards the Concast plant, which started at the level with the yellow service crane on it. This was known to the Concast as the casting floor or 20 m level.

After the steel was tapped into a ladle, the next process was usually secondary steelmaking and the RH degasser. Here the snorkel has been in a ladle, which, when submerged, lifted steel from one side and back through the other by means of a vacuum. A cleaner steel was produced via this process.

Opposite the RH degasser is the SL plant. The Scandinavian Lance was for adding lime and aluminium, among other things, and was part of the secondary steelmaking process. It was essentially a much-improved flushing station.

Above the SL plant, this photograph shows the lances that were used in the process. Inert gas could be forced through the lances, causing the steel in the ladle below to be mixed. At the same time, aluminium wire with calcium or lime in it could be injected into the steel, trimming the chemistry of the steel ready for casting.

The SL plant in operation.

One of the BOS control rooms, which were opposite the vessel. From here, everything in the making of the steel in the vessel was controlled by operators sat in front of various screens.

A ladle of steel on the transfer car at the flushing station in the ladle bay, after what looks like a very lively flush judging by the amount of ejected steel on the floor.

A clear view of the stirring lances and hoods, which take the fumes away, at one of the flushing stations. You can see the little pulpit where the operator would watch and control the process.

Oxygen lances sat in their cradles in the lance shop, where applying new copper tips and other repairs were carried out.

The vessels and transfer cars were still controlled with open electrical contactors, although the speed controllers were much more modern. Of particular note are the knife switches for isolating equipment.

One of the hoods has been moved into the maintenance position to allow access to be gained to the vessel during its relining.

The hood and other hot gas offtakes were made of walls of tubes welded together with cooling water pumped through them. Quite often these tubes burst and poured water into the vessel, which was a problem as water and molten steel could be explosive.

Another view of the hood and cooling water supply hoses, which is in position above the vessel this time.

Scaffolding has been erected around the vessel and men scramble on the plates to repair or replace them.

A view of the BOS vessels after the plant was mothballed. The vessel in the foreground has its skirt lowered onto the vessel mouth.

One of the two clarifiers. Several of the steelmaking operations used a lot of cooling water, as well as water to clean out the gas and the dust that was carried within it. This water eventually returned to these clarifiers, where the dust settled out into sludge.

Vessel operators, and possibly the shift manager, look into the vessel, probably looking at the steel level as it is teemed into the ladle below.

A view of a vessel from the charging side as it starts its blow. Scrap has been charged and molten iron has poured into the vessel. The oxygen lance is then lowered into position above the bath height and high-pressure oxygen is blown onto the bath.

The ladle bay in 2012, although it has an air of a previous time in this black and white picture. The ladle on the preheaters and the high walkways are lit by the light of a ladle being flushed. This is a scene that has some beauty to it in my eye.

Spectacular morning sunlight bursts through the roof openings into the ladle bay. Despite being on a production pause, there was still dust to be blown about if it got windy outside.

A shift engineer releasing the cradle that held a lance that had been lowered by the lance crane onto the carriages. It will then be taken into the lance shop by a winch that pulls the bogey.

Two lances with 'thimbles' still attached. These provided a gas seal around where the lances entered the vessel.

Looking straight up at the lance in the maintenance station, where the skull was burned off that may form on the lance as it was in the vessel. At the top of the plant was the lance crane, the highest at the BOS.

John Noteyoung, an electrical engineer at the BOS plant, racking up a high-voltage circuit breaker in the south substation of the BOS plant. There was a network of circuit breakers that fed different parts of the plant and by switching different ones we could take out breakers for maintenance.

This is a ladle sat in the re-ladle position on the ladle metallurgy furnace (LMF). I don't think this was ever used, so this ladle might just be sat out of the way.

Looking down the teeming bay, the tank degasser is in the middle of the photograph, and was not used during the SSI era.

Torpedoes outside the BOS plant. Some are waiting to go back to the blast furnace, while others are just arriving.

The bloom machine, as seen in the early 1980s with the old style of burning-out platform with the steps at the back. Later modifications enabled access to the platform at each end. The burning-out platform was where the ladle gates and tundishes could be reached. This was a place of danger from the molten steel and an uncomfortable place to be for the casting crew, but this was their place of work and it took some guts to be there at cast start or ladle changes with steel flying about and the constant possibility of a ladle shroud blowing off. You have to have some respect for the lads who did this shift after shift.

The Concast electric shop as it was when I was on day shifts; the doorway went into our rest area, where I learned how to play dominoes. The tea boiler and sink were in the workshop, which definitely would not be allowed now.

A dark photograph of the bloom machine spray chamber showing the 'porcupine'. Water was sprayed through these nozzles as part of the cooling system. This photograph was taken long after the machine was abandoned, but it wasn't much better when operating.

Looking from Slab No. 1 at the bloom machine with the straighteners on the right and the bloom cut-off pulpit just visible in the centre left. In the bottom of the photograph spare moulds and top zones from the slab machines can be seen.

A picture of the bloom-cutting machines (GeGas). The bloom machine was not in use at this time as it was decommissioned following a steel spillage.

The tundish bay, where tundishes were repaired and resprayed, ready to cast on again. This photograph was taken just after a massive clean-up.

Tundishes lined up in the tundish bay. My claim to fame in this photograph is that I fit the two sodium vapour lights at the far end of the bay while I was on the day shift.

These stands were built in the tundish bay to allow a better and safer access to work on the tundishes.

In order to remove the steel skull that was left after the cast finished, the tundish was placed into this machine by crane. It was then clamped and tipped upside down, after which hydraulic rams pushed through the casting opening to shove out the skull. It was always breaking down.

A view of the casting floor from No. 257 feeder crane during our production pause, before we closed again.

A new set of tundishes set up and ready to go on gas in preparation for a cast. The photograph shows a good view of the weir walls and dams inside the tundish. The stopper has a refractory cover around it that was used to keep heat in the stopper when it was on gas, which was a propane flame that went up through the tundish gate from below, heating the ceramic stopper.

Slab No. 2 and the ladle has been opened, the tundish is being filled and the stopper has been opened, allowing steel to flow into the mould. The man on the mould canopy is puddling the molten steel in the mould.

An energetic tundish fill. This was a spectacular sight, but it had its hazards – one being the fire started on top of the tundish car.

A tundish full of steel after a cast. Usually the amount of steel left in the tundish after a cast is much less than here in this photograph. This must have been an aborted cast, which could have been for a number of reasons.

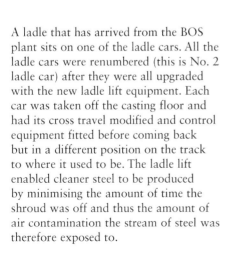

A ladle that has arrived from the BOS plant sits on one of the ladle cars. All the ladle cars were renumbered (this is No. 2 ladle car) after they were all upgraded with the new ladle lift equipment. Each car was taken off the casting floor and had its cross travel modified and control equipment fitted before coming back but in a different position on the track to where it used to be. The ladle lift enabled cleaner steel to be produced by minimising the amount of time the shroud was off and thus the amount of air contamination the stream of steel was therefore exposed to.

Ladle change over, one ladle car has been moved off the machine and an operator cleans out the ladle shroud of oxygen-rich deposits before the next ladle and car are brought into position and the tundish is refilled. By using this method you can keep casting for long periods of time with many ladles in a sequence.

A ladle from the BOS being landed on No. 3 car. You can tell it is being landed because the crank arms have the temporary fibre covers still on that protect the linkages from metal splash.

A view of a pair of tundishes during casting with the ladle shrouds glowing. This is how the molten steel flowed from the ladle to the tundish. Just visible in the tundish is the refractory wall that allowed the steel to flow under it but stopped the effects of turbulence. On the far left is the refractory stopper that controlled the flow from the tundish into the mould below. It is bolted to an arm that is connected to what we called 'the auto', which allowed the stopper to be moved up and down in automatic casting.

Here a tundish car on gas is getting set for casting. The lit gas is blasting up the SEN (submerged entry nozzle) and heating it and the refractories above it in the tundish in order to keep it hot enough that the liquid steel won't chill off and block the tube. The 'auto' (which is a servo motor that drove a shaft in and out that was attached to the stopper) is left disconnected. It would, in use, be fixed vertically.

Two SENs with the gas heaters blasting their flame through the ports and out of the top. During casting these could be changed but they had to be very hot to stop the steel cooling off inside them.

The business end of the ladle gate control. With the aid of the device mounted on the pedestal, the cylinder was offered up to the ladle. Then, pins were put in the top and bottom. The movement of the cylinder pushes the crank arm, which is connected to the gate.

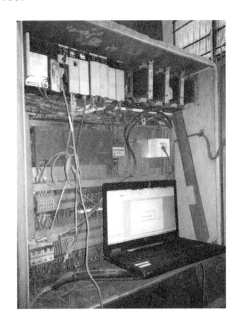

The ladle lift and auto teeming was controlled by a PLC that worked in horrendous conditions for electronics, with dust and heat a continuous problem. Here one of the PLCs is getting the program downloaded after a problem.

Slab No. 2 ladle gates being opened at the start of a cast. This photograph also shows the linkages (top left) that acted upon the gates. Hydraulic cylinders were attached to these linkages and they could be controlled either directly from the ladle car or remotely in a control pulpit.

Slab No. 1 burning-out platform. The operators watch the gates ready to swing the actuators, with the shrouds attached, onto the gate nozzles. This was done with great timing so that the steel flow didn't cool off and stop flowing once the shroud was attached and the gate reopened. If the timing was wrong then it was back off with the shroud to start all over again.

A low-level shot from Slab No. 1 burning-out platform, which was not a place to hang about for too long. I think the two operators are watching the level in the tundish with the far manipulator off the ladle.

Here an operator uses an oxygen lance to blow out the blockages and deposits in a ceramic ladle shroud. This would give the ladle more lives and would be one of the cost-effective measures in use on the plant.

I don't have a photograph of the old style of manipulator, the ones where they were held up onto the ladle gate's nozzle by weights on a cantilever. These manipulators are pneumatic assisted and are held mechanically in place. Although easier to use (so I'm told), the platform was not the best place to be at any time, but especially at the start of a cast or ladle change. Here, two operators fit the shrouds to the ladle gates.

In the foreground are the nozzles of the preheaters for the submerged entry nozzles (SENs). The SENs are the ceramic tubes that allowed the steel to flow into the mould without air getting at the steel; one is just visible glowing hot at the bottom of the tundish car. The middle of the photograph shows the emergency ladle pit (left) and the emergency run off boxes (right). Both were vital when casting as they were designed to hold either a full ladle of steel if there was a problem with the casting ladle, or a tundish-worth of steel if there was a problem with the tundish car, nozzle or stopper in the tundish.

The ladle opens with a shower of sparks as the steel stream hits the inside of the tundish. It was very impressive and bad form to dive into the control room as it happened, although I did step into cover once or twice when it looked a bit heavy!

At the start of a cast, Mark Swan opens the gate with an oxygen lance. On the canopy, bags of starting powder can be seen. I liked this photograph so much that I commissioned a painting in oils of it.

Another view of the same scene but without the sparks of steel flying about. The ladle gates were supposed to run steel as soon as they were opened, but sometimes they didn't and the operator had to stand below the ladle and burn out the steel until it flowed.

The mould operator packs his mould ready for the first SSI cast under the supervision of an experienced mentor. The packing sealed up gaps between the mould and the dummy bar head, and also provided scrap to chill the first steel into the mould and form the hook for withdrawal.

One of the two feeder cranes – this one is No. 257 crane – lands the first full ladle onto the ladle car, ready for the first ever cast of the SSI era, which took place on Wednesday 18 April 2012.

Slab No. 2 and the start of the first SSI cast. This was also the start of so many people's hopes for steelmaking on Teesside. New overalls and fresh paint were evident at the beginning but were soon dulled down.

A contractor monitors the use of refractory materials at the start of the first cast of the SSI era.

A new operator of the SSI era practices using the tundish car. He is holding the manual control of the stopper that is attached to the tundish. This is a good view of the tundish car, showing the gate on the bottom and the 'chicken' button behind the operator, which operated the gate pneumatically.

Casting has been established and the temperature probe is being connected up. What looks like an operator connecting the argon to a bubbler or stopper in the tundish can also be seen.

Another view of a tundish car, with an operator being watched by an experienced operator. In this photograph you can clearly see the casting pendant that allowed the casting operator to control the machine while watching the steel in the mould.

At the end of the cast an operator is seen washing down the mould after capping it off using water. A lot of unused casting powder would have to be cleaned off the mould ready for the next cast.

A safety officer chats to the mould operator on the tundish car. Visits by the safety team became quite an occurrence during the SSI era – a different approach with a newer workforce.

Steelmaking was a twenty-four-hour process and this is Christmas Eve at the Concast plant in 2012.

The Slab No. 1 'auto-teeming' pulpit was used to control the steel flow from the ladle into the tundish. The tundish weight was displayed on an LED display in the middle of the desk and the gates were operated either manually or automatically. The monitors were connected to cameras on the burning-out platform.

Another auto-teeming pulpit, this time looking from the ladle car track above the machine. This one is from Slab No. 2. Visible in the background is the tundish bay, with tundishes getting re-bricked and sprayed with a castable lining.

The mechanical craftsmen remove a mould from Slab No. 2, or they may be refitting it into position. Moulds could be taken out when they'd had enough cast lives and were taken downstairs, where they were maintained or repaired if they had a fault.

No. 257 feeder crane during a maintenance period. Its main hooks are laid out for inspection and some rope work is being carried out on one of the auxiliary hoists.

A shift boilersmith burns some spillage off the mould. This was quite common when a failure in maintaining the correct level would cause the steel in the mould to overflow. This sometimes occurred during auto casting or when a 'flush through' happened, whereby a lump of formed oxide flowed through the SEN into the mould, causing it to rise unexpectedly.

A breakout (loss of containment of the steel in the casting slab). One of the shift boilersmiths burns steel from around the rolls and roll ends to enable the zone – a top zone here – to be removed. This was a bit of a tight squeeze, and claustrophobic.

A view of Slab No. 1 during the 2010 shutdown of steelmaking. From this control room side you can see the moulds, the tundish cars in their ambush positions and the burning-out platform with the shroud manipulators.

A very dusty casting floor; either it was very windy or there has been a problem at the BOS plant, with clouds of fumes slowly moving onto the casting floor. On the left is a removed top zone with the remains of a breakout slab still inside. It is waiting to be lowered down to the ground floor, where it will be placed into a waiting transfer car. It would have to have the slab removed first though.

Ladle car No. 5. From this side the hydraulics and the back of the PLC cabinet can be seen. The triangular stop prevented the cars from physically going any further along the bay.

Another view of the Slab No. 1 moulds. The moulds were covered by these lids, which stopped all the steam out of the spray chamber from coming up and restricting the view of the mould level. The ends of the mould were free to move in and out automatically during casting in later years, but originally we had to stop casting to change size.

A Slab No. 2 cast emerging from the straightener. In view is the hook that was formed in the mould when the cast started. It allowed the steel strand to be withdrawn from the machine driven by the straightener motors.

Casting a continuous steel slab. The steel emerges from the last straightener segment and moves on to the cutting machines to the right, which is out of frame.

The Slab No. 2 GeGa cutting machine in operation. Here, the beam with the feet drops onto the slab, allowing the whole machine to move with the slab. Two burner carriages move across the slab, cutting it to length.

Slab No. 1 cutting machines. After being cut to length the slab would continue on the roller table to the marker machine. It would then pass on to be picked up by one of the cranes.

A continuous-cast slab travels over water-cooled rolls behind the cutting machines. There was a device here that counted the amount of revolutions of the roll and so the length of slab emerging under the cutting machine was determined.

The Slab No. 1 cut-off pulpit was refurbished for the SSI start up, with new desks and new control screens. These were much less cluttered than the old desks with their buttons and lamps.

Slab No. 1's cutting machines in the ambush position, with the winch platform above.

The control pulpit of the Slab
No. 1 straightener. Slab No. 1 had
computer-controlled controls, with these
screens indicating the position of the
straightener. It is still covered in the sheeting
applied after the mothballing in 2010.

The Slab No. 1 casting control room, with the same system as the straightener showing on the screens. This time, the system was to control the casting machine.

The Slab No. 2 straightener control pulpit was almost on top of the casting slab, which made this a very warm place when casting. The motors on the right of the picture are the straightener motors, which moved the casting slab through the machine.

The Slab No. 1 winch platform. The winch drums and winch motors are at the back of the platform and the cut-off pulpit is just visible behind.

The dummy bar connected to the dummy bar chain ready to go into the straightener. With this in the mould and sealing the bottom you could continuously cast. At this point during casting this ramp would move up and out of the way of the slab.

Slab No. 1 and some leading links next to the straightener, which connected the head to the chain. Straightener motors can be seen to the left and the stairs to the machine are on the right of this photograph.

The mechanical craftsmen of the Concast plant slide a refurbished strand guide into place on one of the casting machines. This took a lot of climbing – it stood about 10 metres up – but in later years they had harnesses.

After the slab was cut to length, it was marked with a sprayed aluminium number ready for dispatch. Here, the marker carriage is out and spraying a number to the side of the slab.

A slab that has been chosen for a length check is placed on a table to be manually measured. This was used to tell if the electronic one was accurate or not!

The view of the export bay just before the shutdown in 2010. This image was taken on my last night shift and the gloom and debris lying about summed up the mood.

The same view of the export bay, but the conditions were much improved at the start of the SSI era: tidy, with new rolls and painted.

No. 184 crane and slabs in the cooling bay. No. 185 crane can be seen in the distance. This is from the time before the discharge rail link was laid along the right of this photograph.

A view from Slab No. 1 cut off, looking towards the Slab No. 2 discharge roller tables and No. 184 crane. The 'boxes' that the slabs are entering were the de-bearders, which removed the 'beard' formed when the slab was cut. These would cause problems if they were left on and were rolled into the slab.

At Slab No. 2, Strand No. 2, the spray chamber door opened for the changing of a strand guide segment. The Segment would be lowered onto a carriage that was moved up and down to the correct position.

Three reconditioned strand guide segments. During the restart all the segments were removed and refurbished before being put back in again.

Another view inside the spray chamber, showing a different style of strand guide segments.

The workshop at Slab No. 2, where the actuators were maintained. One actuator is seen in the vice, undergoing a repair. It is unusually very tidy.

The Concast workshop on a night shift, with no one about. This was where the moulds and top zones were repaired in the stands, especially when the WAM (automatic width adjustment) was playing up.

During restart we had problems with the variable speed drives on each ladle car. Here, the panel doors are open, showing the directional control equipment being repaired.

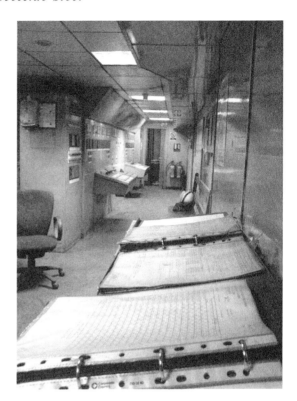

The Slab No. 2 control room. In the foreground are folders of casting parameters and in the distance are all the control switches and indication instruments vital for the operator to monitor what is happening with the casting machine.

A view behind the panels of Slab No. 2 control room, showing PLCs and instruments that controlled the waters, gas and the casting machine's control switches.

A view of the water-cooling system of the mould and also the spray water system on the top zone segment. The top zone is just below the mould (the mould has the junction boxes on it).

Nos 2 and 3 slitting machines at ambush position in front of the slitting pulpit in the Concast export bay. One man operated all four beds.

In the export bay the slabs were prepared for sending out, usually by train. Nominated slabs had a sample cut from them, which was sent for analysis to check against the reported cast records. Here, an operator cuts out a sample with a stihl saw.

A view from the back of the Concast, looking at the water treatment plant cooling towers and the scale pit crane.

The back of the Concast plant, showing the conveyor that took lime and other materials up to the bunkers at the top of the BOS plant. On the right is the end of the slag bay gantry.

A line of lime wagons deliver lime to the underground bunkers at the lime shed. Eventually this system was stopped and road wagons were used to carry out the delivery instead.

A scrap car with empty scrap pans in the scrap bay. The scrap might be bales of cans or offcuts from beams. These were loaded into the cars by magnet cranes.

Scrap pans on a car on the charging side of the vessels. The pans look empty, so they could have just charged the scrap into the vessel that is just visible to the left of the car.

A very dusty view from inside No. 4 belt as it transferred lime up to the BOS high line bunkers. This belt originated from below ground, where the lime was kept.

A scrap car loaded with full scrap pans is caught in the evening sun as it enters the BOS plant.

Looking into the export bay from the bridge into the office block. This image is from 2012, just before the restart and the first slab, so everything is tidy and newly painted. This is the spot from where the press and invited guests watched the first cast slab roll down the discharge table. I remember it well, as the roller table tripped out and I had to dash into the sub to reset them!

Slab No. 2, Strand No. 2, and the first cut into the first slab of the SSI era. What is not apparent is Peter Noteyoung, the plant engineer, faking the limits to keep the machine in the cutting position.

Concast was set up to cast 9-, 10- and 12-inch-thick slabs, but during the SSI years we started to cast 8-inch slabs. This was the first slab we cast at that thickness.

A very grey day and slag that has been tipped into a slag pen is in the process of being dug out, ready for recycling.

A night shift is lit up as a slag pot is being tipped into a slag pen and the steam coming from previously tipped slag pots are making a very atmospheric picture.

The BOS plant in 2011 and a new stack is being fitted after the old one collapsed almost into the scrap bay. This was not the first time that a chimney had collapsed; the first one, some time ago, took part of the scrap bay with it.

BOS chimneys from the slag bay. With the scrap bay in the background, the scrap car tracks can be seen running from the right to the left.

These huge chimneys took away the carbon monoxide gas from the steelmaking process. Ignited at the top of the stack, it was a constant sight at Teesside.

A slag pot being tipped in the slag bay. Sometimes if the pit had water in it or was damp the slag would explode; in fact, it has been known to clear the back sheeting line and set fire to the diesel tank in that roadway.

Slag pots stored in the slag bay, ready for use. An old ingot mould from the period when the BOS plant used to cast ingots sits behind the pots. This was prior to when the continuous-casting plant was built.

Loco No. 268 on the tracks where all the wagons were organised before dispatch. It still has the Corus logo but is missing its nameplate. The locos were named after ironstone mines, I believe.

In 2008 a full torpedo ladle derailed just before the bend into the BOS plant. It took three heavy lift cranes to lift the torpedo and refit the bogies.

Many a bloom has left the Concast plant via this track. On the left is the Concast office block and on the right is the export bay. Connecting them both is the bridge into the plant.

A last rake of wagons waits to be loaded up with the last slabs that were still in the export bay, with no more work to be done.